# The 60's & 7
# Rock Score.

**Wise Publications**
London/New York/Sydney

Exclusive distributors:
**Music Sales Limited**
8/9 Frith Street, London W1V 5TZ, England.

**Music Sales Pty Limited**
120 Rothschild Avenue, Rosebery, NSW 2018, Australia.

This book © Copyright 1989 by
Wise Publications
UK ISBN 0.7119.1668.3
Order No. AM72620

Layout by Tim Field
Compiled by Peter Evans

Music Sales' complete catalogue lists thousands of
titles and is free from your local music shop, or direct from
Music Sales Limited. Please send £1 in stamps for postage to
Music Sales Limited, 8/9 Frith Street, London W1V 5TZ.

Printed and bound in Great Britain by
Courier International Ltd, Tiptree, Essex

**ALL RIGHT NOW 4**
**(FREE)**

**A WHITER SHADE OF PALE 64**
**(PROCOL HARUM)**

**BUS STOP 59**
**(THE HOLLIES)**

**GET IT ON 13**
**(T. REX)**

**LET'S SPEND THE NIGHT TOGETHER 70**
**(THE ROLLING STONES)**

**MY GENERATION 37**
**(THE WHO)**

**PARANOID 20**
**(BLACK SABBATH)**

**SMOKE ON THE WATER 26**
**(DEEP PURPLE)**

**WHILE MY GUITAR GENTLY WEEPS 46**
**(THE BEATLES)**

# ALL RIGHT NOW

## Words & Music by Paul Rodgers & Andy Fraser

5

wait _____ or hes-i-tate _____ Let's move be - fore they raise the parking _____ rate" Oh,
"Love _____ Lord above _____ now you're tryin' to Trick me in love" Oh,

All right now _____ ba - by it's all - right _____ now _____

All right now _____ ba - by it's all - right _____ now _____

10

# GET IT ON

Words & Music by Marc Bolan

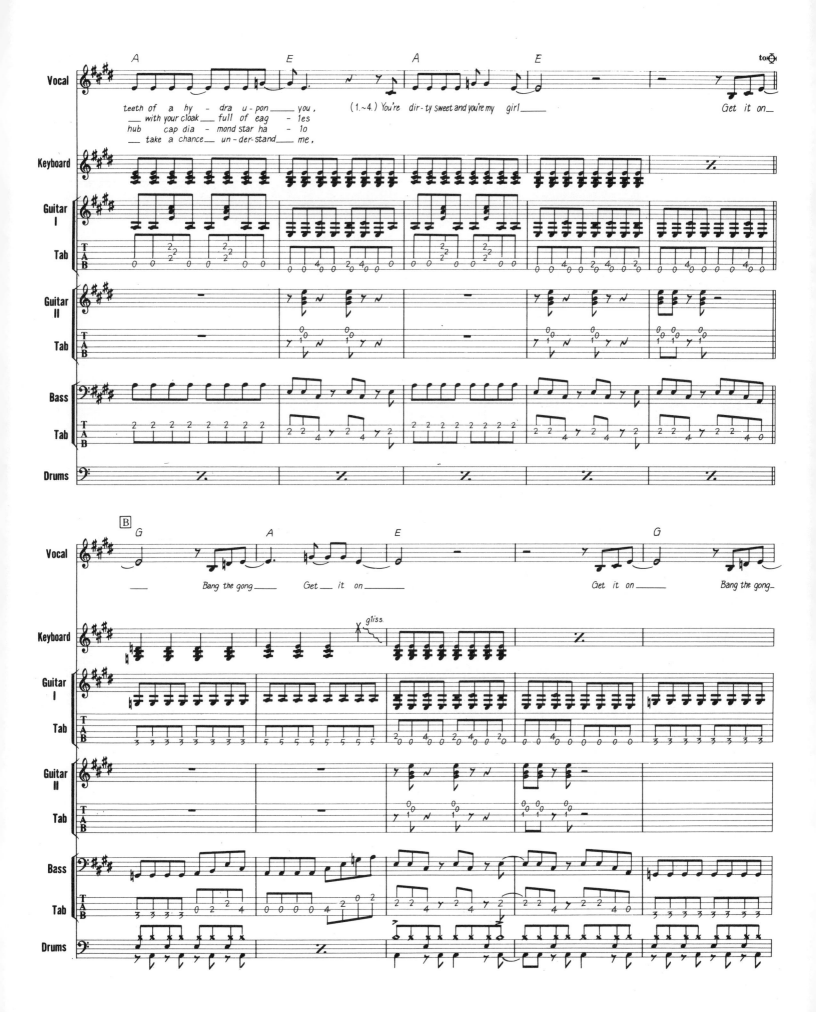

get___ it__ on ___

Well, you're built___
Well, you're win -

Fade Out

19

# PARANOID

### Words & Music by Terence Butler, John Osbourne, Frank Iommi & William Ward

21

24

# SMOKE ON THE WATER

Words & Music by Ian Gillan, Ritchie Blackmore, Jon Lord, Roger Glover & Ian Paice

Smoke    on the wat — er

Fade Out

# MY GENERATION

Words & Music by Pete Townshend

My, my yeah, gen-er-a-tion My, my, my,

my

gen-er-a-tion

Peo-ple try to put us down _____
(The) things they do look awful cold _____

Talk-in' 'bout my gen-er-a-tion

Just be-cause we g-
(I) hope I die before

44

# WHILE MY GUITAR GENTLY WEEPS

Words & Music by George Harrison

I don't know why_____ no - bod- y told_____ you_____
I__ don't know how_____ you__ were de - vert - ed,

how__ to un - fold_____ your love._____
you__ were per - vert - ed _____ too.

I don't know how _____ some___one con - trolled you
I don't know how _____ you___were in - vert - ed

they___bought and sold _____ you.
no___one a - lert - ed _____ you. _____ I look
I look

D.S.

# BUS STOP

### Words & Music by Graham Gouldman

All the peo-ple stare__ As if we were__ both quite in-sane Some-day my name__

__ and her's are go-ing to be the same __

(Tambourine)

# A WHITER SHADE OF PALE

Words & Music by Keith Reid & Gary Brooker

We skipped the light____ fan-dan-go _____
She said "There____ is no rea-son _____

(And) turned__ cart-wheels__ cross the floor____
And____ the truth is plain to see"____

# LET'S SPEND THE NIGHT TOGETHER

*Words & Music by Mick Jagger & Keith Richard*

1.) Now don't you worry 'bout what's on your mind__ Oh__ no__    I'm in no hurry   I could
2.3.) I feel so strong (that) I can't dis - guise__ Oh__ no__    But I just   won't a-

Vocal: Let's spend the night ___ to - ge - ther

Now I need you more ___ than e - ver    Let's spend the night ___ to-ge-ther    Let's spend the night ___
(now ___ )

Vocal lyrics line 1: I need you more___ than e-ver    Let's spend the night___ to-ge-ther    Let's spend the night___

Vocal lyrics line 2: ___ to-ge-ther ___ now ___    yeah ___

D. S. al Coda

3x Repeat ( 2,3x : Simile )

Let's spend the night _____ to-ge-ther    Now I need you more _____ than e - ver    Let's spend the night _____

to - ge - ther    now _____